OLD WOODY
LOSES HIS CAT

CANDLE
BOOKS

It was a beautiful summer day.
'I'm going fishing,' said Old Woody.
He packed his fishing-rod and his net, and set off
with Filbert the cat.

Old Woody knew a quiet spot where the fishing was excellent. He cast his line and waited for the fish to bite.
Suddenly Filbert caught sight of a brightly coloured butterfly.

Old Woody's float vanished beneath the water. He had a bite! Old Woody gripped his rod and pulled as hard as he could. The fish wriggled and jerked. What a mighty fish it must be!

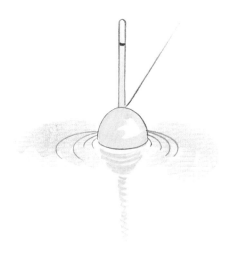

Crrrrack! Woody's rod snapped in two.
'Help, shouted Old Woody. 'I'm falling in!'
He tried to grab on to something – but there was
nothing within reach. With a mighty ker-splash
he toppled into the pond.

Old Woody got a real soaking. He was so wet –
and so cold.
'Where's my rod?' he wailed. 'And where are my
glasses? . . . And where's Filbert?'

Filbert had absolutely no idea what was happening to Woody. She was far away – and interested only in the butterfly. She followed the butterfly wherever it went – further and further and . . .

By a bit of luck, Old Woody found his glasses. He gave them a rub, then started to look for Filbert. 'Where *has* she got to?' he asked. 'She never goes off on her own. I *do* hope she's all right.'

Woody noticed a hollow tree.

Perhaps Filbert has crept in there, he thought.

He peered gingerly inside. No – she wasn't in the hollow tree.

But Woody didn't notice hundreds of little eyes watching him.

Suddenly a furious swarm of bees flew at Woody. They lived in a nearby tree, and Old Woody had wandered just a bit too close.
Old Woody raced off as fast as his legs could carry him.

Woody ran deep, deep into the wood. At last he shook off the angry bees.

When he had his breath back, he started to shout:

'Filbert, Filbert – where are you. . . Filbert?'

But there was no answer.

By now Old Woody was *really* worried.

Woody decided to climb a very tall tree. From its top branches he could see a long way. Old Woody peered into the distance, gazing in every direction.

Suddenly he gasped. There was Filbert – and she was in big trouble!

Filbert was clinging onto a branch on the very edge of a cliff. If she were to fall . . .

Old Woody was down the tree and at Filbert's side in no time at all. He lay down, stretched out on his tummy, and grabbed hold of Filbert. Very gently, Old Woody pulled the cat to safety.

Hooray! Filbert was safe and sound. Old Woody was so happy. And naturally, Filbert was pretty happy too.
Woody gave Filbert a huge hug, and tickled her tummy. His precious Filbert was back with him.

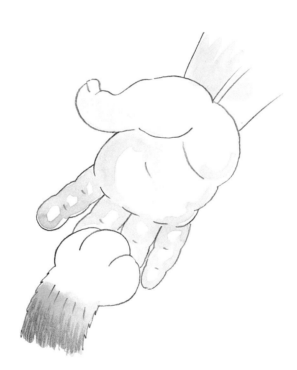

Poor Filbert was still feeling very shaky, so Old Woody carried her home in his fishing net.
When they reached home, Old Woody gave Filbert the cat a tasty fish. Soon Filbert would be strong and fit again

'Now we must have a party!' said Old Woody. 'We'll invite all the cats we know. It'll be a party no one will ever forget – because Filbert was lost, and now she's safe home again!'

This story about Old Woody and his cat Filbert is similar to a story Jesus told about a lost sheep. You can read it in your Bible in Luke 15:1-7. Jesus said, 'Because God loves you so much, he comes looking for you when you run away from him.'